Introduction

Technological development is acknowledged as a major impetus to continued economic growth and business expansion. The role of new, and especially the generic, technologies is seen as particularly important. They can act as the seeds of major new sectors with prospects of significant growth and higher profitability. For developed countries, establishing a leading position in such innovative technologies may be critical as more established industries mature and competitive advantage shifts to countries with *inter alia* access to cheaper factors of production.

Innovation has long been recognised as crucial to the continued survival of businesses in a climate where rivalry and change is intense. There is forever the incentive for businesses to introduce change, to attempt to differentiate their offerings in some way, to find a means of establishing some proprietary position. For the business then:

> " ... the appropriate perspective is of struggle and rivalry ... Superior product and process technology is a basis for superior profitability that in turn gives the firm potential advantages in all those competition enhancing activities which require an investment of resources" (1).

Such rivalry occurs not only between businesses in similar product markets; it can arise from those operating in other product markets; whilst the prospects of competition from as yet unknown sources is a continuing discipline to those with tendencies towards complacency and quasi-monopoly behaviour. Schumpeter saw this as a major feature of capitalist competition:

> "It is hardly necessary to point out that competition of the kind we now have in mind acts not only when in being but also when it is merely an ever present threat. It disciplines before it attacks. The businessman feels himself to be in a competitive situation even if he is alone in his field" (2).

Therefore, in the constant search to secure some competitive edge, businesses must be continuously engaged on a process of improvement, modification and innovation, even where their own activities might undermine the bases of existing operations. A failure to do so where there are so many potential sources of change which might erode the foundations on which they compete can only result in a gradual, at best, loss of competitiveness.

This emphasis on rivalry does not, however, exclude the possibilities of various forms of collaborative activity even amongst those businesses which *prima facie* might appear to be in competition with one another. The history of industrial development is marked by various forms of legitimate and fruitful associations between firms, entered into often to assist them in being more competitive. The large number of contemporary strategic alliances and other forms of co-operation are a continuation of this trend although there does appear to have been a general intensification of this form of activity, compelled in no minor part by the changing nature of technology. Similarly, the wide range of pre-competitive R&D initiatives do not suggest an underpinning of this view of competitive rivalry. Such co-operation in fact can be seen as yielding generic scientific and technological knowledge which businesses then employ to develop differentiated products using knowledge and assets unique to themselves.

Increasingly, businesses are viewed not as autonomous units but as constituents of networks embracing universities, consultancies, their materials, components and equipment suppliers, distribution intermediaries and customers and users (3). These networks can involve complex sets of relationships and involve various flows of information, a sharing of activities and different forms of collaboration. Corporate behaviour will often be shaped and modified by

other members of the networks of which the business is a part. Network formation and positioning may well be an important contributor to competitiveness. As Jarillo has argued:

> "If a firm is able to obtain an arrangement whereby it 'farms out' activities to the most efficient supplier, keeps for itself that activity in which it has a comparative advantage and lowers transaction costs, a superior 'mode of organisation' emerges: the strategic network" (4).

One compelling reason for participation in the development and use of networks is to ensure effective innovation. The reasons for engaging with potential customers and users are already clear from the numerous studies of innovative activity that point to a customer orientation being an important feature of successful innovators. Other studies have also highlighted the active role of users as a source of ideas and new developments (5). It would appear a sensible means of ensuring that a user dimension is injected into the innovation process. In addition, the need for firms to adopt an extrovert stance, searching for and readily accepting information from a diverse range of external sources has also been pinpointed (6).

The competitiveness of businesses involved in nascent sectors, such as those founded on new technology, might be particularly dependent on the positioning in a network of sound relationships with 'progressive' potential customers and users, leading suppliers and so on. Such embryonic sectors are likely to be highly energetic, encountering significant technological change, rapid rates of market development and considerable uncertainty. Much remains unformed and unclear. Networking activity is likely to be stochastic, and networks unstable and often informal. The involvement of established, even large, firms in such sectors is unlikely to have a marked tempering effect, since they often form separate ventures that assume responsibility for the development of their interests there. These often have

many of the features of the smaller start up businesses. The options of building on prior experience and relationships are of course open to all those involved.

There is an additional feature of such networking in nascent sectors: it is likely to focus on technology development and the product rather than the benefits sought by potential customers. Often those initially involved are driven by enthusiasm for the technology and the product. They see rich technological prospects which need to be reaped and they are concerned with the direction and development of the technology itself, in the face of many uncertainties and possible technical difficulties, towards something which can be marketed and sold. Nevertheless, in some cases, obsession with the technology may hazard the successful attainment of the business' objectives. Indeed, the early participants in the development of the sector may find that they provide the opportunities for later entrants which may benefit from the experience of these pioneers.

This paper outlines some of the issues associated with the development of a nascent sector, using 'mobile communications' as an example. The intrinsic instability of the early networking activities is highlighted, as are the difficulties flowing from an over-emphasis on technological development, at the expense of attention to customer values.

'SUCCESSFUL' INNOVATION

Numerous studies of the factors affecting the outcomes of technological innovations (7, 8, 9, 10) have suggested that there are several factors which seem to discriminate between

successful and failed outcomes. Rothwell, in a review of the results of a number of studies

on innovation, highlights some of the factors associated with success in industrial

innovation (11).

Table 1: Rothwell's Factors Associated with Successful Innovation

Marketing and user needs
Innovation as a corporate wide task
Efficient development work
Planning and management techniques
Quality of management, personnel policy and management style
Good communication and effective collaboration
After sales service and user education
Key individuals

It is apparent that innovations are more likely to be adopted if they satisfy the requirements

of potential customers/users and if careful attention is directed to various marketing

considerations.

Rothwell describes a concern with marketing and user needs as the area which is most crucial

in determining innovative success or failure. He goes on to state that:

> " ... the majority of successful innovations arise in response to the recognition
> of a need of one sort or another as opposed to the recognition of a new
> technical potential ... failure is associated with the 'we know best' attitude
> which is fairly common among technical inventors, who often fail to see the
> need to consult potential users concerning their invention" (11).

The active involvement of targeted customers in product development is one obvious means of possibly securing the requisite customer orientation. McKenna suggests the need for manufacturers to develop close relationships with customers in technological development, advising businesses to consider:

> " ... integrating the customer into the design process to guarantee a product that is tailored not only to the customers' needs and desires but also to the customers' strategies" (12).

In addition, the widely diverse sources of information, the rapid rate of, for example, technological change and the unpredictable nature of technological development suggest that an over-emphasis on internal information and development may not only result in missed opportunities, but may also lead to inefficient development. First, customers can act as a rich source of new products (5). Second, Rothwell emphasises the contribution of good and efficient communication to successful industrial innovation, stating that:

> " ... successful innovators, while enjoying good intra-firm communication, establish efficient communication links with outside scientific and technical establishments and make deliberate efforts to survey potentially useful externally generated ideas" (11).

A business can be regarded as being a component of a network embracing suppliers, customers and other parties, such as universities and consultancies. Such networks may involve active interaction between various parties such as in the development of new products. Thus, as Axelsson and Hakansson point out:

> "....product development as an interaction process means that the resources of a single company in terms of technology, personnel, etc., are combined with the resources of one or more external units" (13).

The current vogue for 'strategic alliances' (14) accords with a pattern of networking; and the apparent increased emphasis on collaboration may reflect several, not mutually exclusive, trends:

- the convergence of diverse technologies;
- an increasing pace of change mirrored in shortening product life cycles;
- the consequent need to market widely and rapidly; and
- greater costs and risks of innovation in many sectors.

Collaborations as a means of enhancing the effectiveness and efficiency of technological development has become an integral part of the 'received wisdom' or industry 'recipe' (15) of many sectors. Beliefs such as those on the critical importance of collaborative activity, form the 'sector paradigm' (16) and are reinforced by *inter alia*, interaction between sector participants.

NEW TECHNOLOGY SECTORS

We have already referred to the importance of new technology based sectors. In general, we believe that they exhibit a number of significant features. They will tend to be technologically energetic, with rapid advances in technological frontiers, leaving in their wake rich opportunities for product innovations; to have high rates of product obsolescence; and to exhibit rapid, if somewhat erratic, rates of growth (17). The most dominant feature is likely to be uncertainty which surrounds:

- the product specifications acceptable to customers;
- the optimum technological trajectory, (18) given that there may be several from which to select;
- the customer segments which will be most profitable;
- the intensity of competition; and
- the breadth of the 'competitive field'.

Although there is considerable questioning *per se* of many of the traditional textbook approaches to business strategy formulation and management, these methodologies are likely to be even more inappropriate to 'nascent' sectors given the significant uncertainties and the fast rate of change.

PROPOSITIONS

Against this background we suggest a number of propositions regarding product development in such 'nascent' sectors, and we will then hope to illustrate some of the issues involved by considering 'mobile communications'.

Proposition 1: **The rapid change in nascent sectors implies that entrepreneurial action tends to be the initial spur to development.** We take as given that new technology based sectors, certainly in their early phases, exhibit above average rates of change. There is evidence to support this for new technology sectors as a whole (19) and our own research reinforces this. The opportunity for detailed analysis, together with the dearth of reliable and consistent data, suggest that traditional strategic planning methodologies will tend not to be pursued and that 'bold', risk taking behaviour is more the norm.

Proposition 2: **Collaboration is regarded as increasingly important for product development.** Business will seek to form relationships with a view to constructing networks that in some way provide them with proprietorial access to resources and information. The rationale underpinning the emphasis on collaborative activity has already been outlined.

Proposition 3: **The development of networks will be primarily opportunistic in nascent sectors.** This is a logical deduction from proposition 1. Given limited knowledge and the need to act rapidly, optimum action will generally involve capitalising on what is known and what is encountered at the time.

Proposition 4: **Technological and product development is the essential driver of nascent new technology sectors.** The reasons include those outlined above. Such sectors tend to be dominated by: the enthusiasm of technologists; a consequent urge for technological pioneering and excellence; and the practical considerations of developing an offering that can be sold. The major risk of this 'technology/product' focus is a consequent lack of attention not only to customer values (the presence of marketers is often sadly lacking) but also to the development of appropriate systems, particularly with regard to financial planning and control, that ultimately can lead to the collapse of many of the new businesses.

Proposition 5: **Networks in nascent new technology sectors are intrinsically unstable.** The fact that such sectors are dynamic, that responses are often *ad hoc* rather than considered and that in the case of collaborative activities they may not necessarily be primarily driven by rational business considerations, suggests that network relationships will be transient, and will often be informal. With the widening availability of information, organisational learning and further technological and possible market development, the scope and type of relationships and the rationale underpinning them may change. Sectoral evolution is also likely to shift emphasis from, say, technological development to marketing issues, which may also have implications for collaborative activities.

Proposition 6: **There will be a consolidation of the network over time, with a coalescence around stronger parties.** In the early phases of sectoral development, there will often be considerable interest from many organisations. Some will engage in tentative involvement with the aim of exploring the possible potential; others will hope to secure some short term gain; and yet others may aim to establish a longer term position. As the sector develops, the nature of the commitments and the possible returns clarifies. Some will be unable to sustain a position and be forced to exit; whilst some will realise the value of their stakes. Others will often aim to effect rationalisation through mergers and acquisitions, a process which may be assisted by later entrants, either through their active participation in the process or as a reaction to the threat they present. These forces drive the consolidation of the network, but any realised equilibrium must be apparent, because at some later stage further technological development is likely to disrupt such stability.

These propositions will be addressed with regard to the mobile communications sector which in its relatively short life has itself undergone significant changes that have widened the technological scope of the sector, broadened its competitive field and enhanced the nature, and increased the diversity of the market offerings.

METHODOLOGY

The mobile communications sector has been studied from 1988 to the present date using both secondary and primary research information sources. The secondary research, which has been done throughout the length of the study, has involved analysis of material such as consultants' reports, news reports, journal articles and background material from the

organisations involved in the study. The primary research has involved personal semi-structured interviews with senior representatives of each of the various consortia operating in the cellular radio, telepoint and PCN sectors. From 1988 to the present, a total of 29 senior executives from 22 organisations with an interest in these sectors have been interviewed on often two or more occasions during this period. Apart from the schedule of personal interviews, two extensive mail questionnaire surveys of existing and potential mobile communications customers have been carried out. A mail questionnaire has also been sent to those members of the cellular radio, telepoint and PCN consortia which were not personally interviewed.

MOBILE COMMUNICATIONS

The Technologies

Mobile communications embraces a wide range of technologies including cellular radio, radiopaging, Personal Mobile Radio (PMR), telepoint and Personal Communications Networks (PCNs). The linking factor between these systems is that they all meet the need to communicate whilst on the move, or away from a fixed line terminal. The rivalry between these technologies constitutes *major design competition*.

The origins of the UK mobile communications sector can be traced back to over 40 years ago when organisations first began to use proprietary radio systems, closed user networks known as Personal Mobile Radio (PMR). Following shortly afterwards, in 1956, paging came onto the market in its most basic form, as a hospital 'bleeper' system. Both paging and PMR

eventually evolved into national mobile communications facilities. Until fairly recently, the mobile communications market, based on these two technologies, was relatively staid and unexciting. This changed with the introduction of cellular radio in 1985. Cellular radio was the first genuinely two-way mobile service available to UK users. In this paper, however, we concentrate on the newest mobile technologies of telepoint and PCN, but also refer briefly to the technology of cellular radio. Therefore, the technologies of cellular radio, telepoint and PCN will all be briefly described here.

CELLULAR RADIO

Cellular radio uses both radio technology and more traditional telephone systems to transmit signals to any fixed phone in the world, or to any mobile phone in the area served by either of the two UK cellular radio networks. Each of the networks divides the country into cells. These are areas, which may be as small as 1km in radius, that are each equipped with a base station containing a low powered radio transmitter and receiver. Calls from cellular telephones are received at these base stations and passed on to a regional exchange, which connects them to the fixed line network, or back to a base station if the call is to another cellular phone. Two operators, Cellnet and Vodafone, launched their cellular radio services in 1985.

TELEPOINT

Telepoint is based upon second generation cordless telephone technology (CT2). The service consists of pocket sized cordless telephone handsets which can connect via a radio link to

publicly sited base stations. Through these base stations, calls are connected to the BT or Mercury telephone network. Calls on telepoint handsets must be made within approximately 200 metres of a base station. Telepoint does not have the capacity to receive incoming calls. It is a one way service only, although, as with established cordless telephones, base units can be purchased in order to receive calls in the home. Four operating consortia were licensed in January 1989 to provide telepoint services in the UK. Three of these launched a telepoint service in 1990 but all have subsequently withdrawn the service due to the low numbers of subscribers attracted.

PERSONAL COMMUNICATIONS NETWORKS

PCNs are, to an extent, a development along the same technological trajectory as cellular radio. Both of these technologies operate on the basis of a national network of base stations, each contained within an area termed a cell where calls are received before being passed onto a regional exchange where they are connected into the fixed line network or back to another cell. The difference between cellular radio and PCNs relates to the scale of the respective infrastructures and the size of handsets. PCNs will operate at much higher frequencies and therefore the cells will be much smaller as signals between base stations and telephone cannot cover such a long distance. This allows for smaller, cheaper handsets needing less battery power than cellular radio handsets, as the signals do not have to travel so far. Three operators were licensed in December 1989 to provide PCN services in the UK. PCNs are still in the product development stage and commercial services are unlikely to be launched for some time.

MARKET DEVELOPMENT

The mobile communications market was greatly stimulated by the launch of cellular radio services in 1985. When the cellular networks became available, there followed dramatic and explosive market growth at a level far higher than originally predicted and until relatively recently, growth in demand consistently exceeded forecasts. This may have been due in part to the imposed structure of the market, where there are duopoly network operators and a channel system based on competing service providers and dealers. One result of the success of cellular radio was that businesses queued up to enter what they saw as a highly lucrative market. For this reason, both the telepoint and PCN licence applications were heavily oversubscribed. Businesses responded eagerly within a limited time frame to these opportunities to enter the mobile communications market, indicative of what might be termed 'entrepreneurial swarming' activity and the urge to establish a position in the highly profitable mobile communications market.

In the case of telepoint, initial forecasts of growth suggested a market worth £1 billion per year in the early 1990s, with an estimated 3.6 million subscribers by 1995 (20). The experience of the telepoint operators so far suggests that such optimism was considerably misplaced. Market reaction to the launch of telepoint services by three of the operators involved has been unenthusiastic and the rate of acceptance of the technology disappointing. In July 1991, there existed less than 10,000 telepoint subscribers (20). The three operators to launch a telepoint service, Mercury Callpoint, Ferranti and Phonepoint, have all since withdrawn from the market, leaving only Hutchison to consider whether to launch at all.

INTER-ORGANISATIONAL RELATIONSHIPS

The pattern in the mobile communications sector has been for organisations to group together in order to bid for operating licences, reflecting Littler and Wilson's observation of a recent increase in strategic alliancing between organisations (14).

Within each major design configuration, various consortia have been formed to provide rival services. In January 1989, four consortia were licensed to provide telepoint services in the UK. These were Phonepoint (a consortium of British Telecom, STC, Deutsche Bundespost, France Telecom and Nynex); Zonephone (a consortium led by Ferranti and also including a number of small venture capitalists); Mercury Callpoint (a consortium of Mercury Communications, Motorola and Shaye Communications) and BYPS (originally a consortium of Barclays, Philips and Shell).

In December 1989, three operators were licensed to provide PCN services. These were Mercury PCN (a consortium of Mercury Communications, Motorola and Telefonica); Unitel (a consortium originally composed of STC, Thorn EMI, US West and Deutsche Bundespost) and Microtel (originally a consortium of British Aerospace, Pacific Telesis, Millicom, Matra and Sony).

The over-riding reason for collaborations in the mobile communications sector, and for telepoint and PCN in particular, was that of gaining access to technology and experience.

Businesses formed relationships with those organisations considered most likely to have the skills and expertise necessary to gain a telepoint or PCN licence. Few of the consortia have remained unchanged. Many organisations have left the telepoint and PCN sector altogether and many of those remaining have found it necessary to seek new partners. The changes in consortium formation since the licences were initially awarded is shown diagrammatically in Figures 1 and 2 and is also outlined in more detail in the Appendix.

The way in which consortia network relationships have been formed and subsequently changed is best examined by looking in more detail at the history and composition of a number of the telepoint and PCN consortia as follows. The precise changes in the composition of all of the telepoint and PCN consortia are described in the Appendix.

Figure 1: Changes in Telepoint Consortia since January 1989

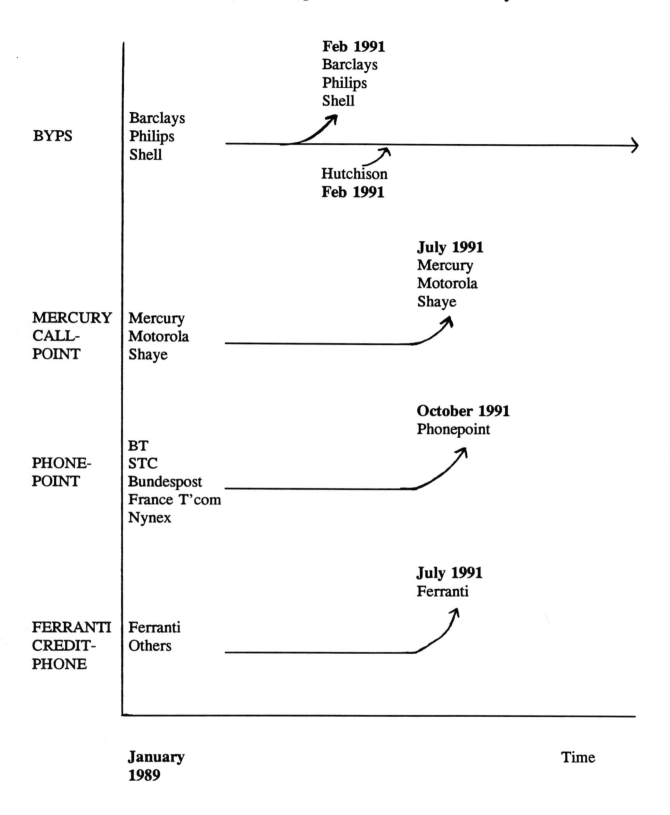

Key

Entrants to/exits from the market

19

Figure 2: Changes in the PCN Consortia since December 1989

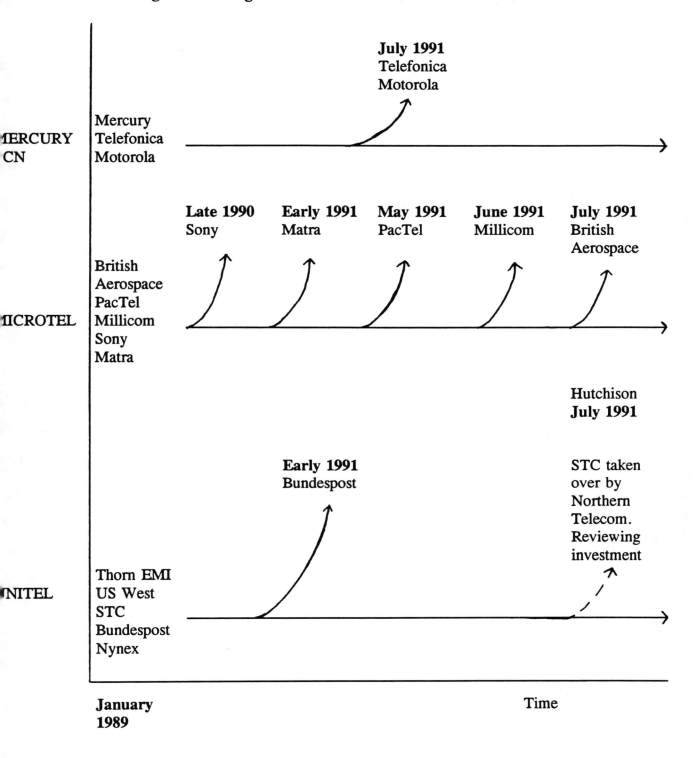

MERCURY PCN
Mercury
Telefonica
Motorola

July 1991
Telefonica
Motorola

MICROTEL
British
Aerospace
PacTel
Millicom
Sony
Matra

Late 1990
Sony

Early 1991
Matra

May 1991
PacTel

June 1991
Millicom

July 1991
British
Aerospace

Hutchison
July 1991

STC taken
over by
Northern
Telecom.
Reviewing
investment

Early 1991
Bundespost

UNITEL
Thorn EMI
US West
STC
Bundespost
Nynex

**January
1989**

Time

Key

Entrants to/exits from the market

Case 1: Mercury Callpoint

Original consortium participants: **Mercury Communications, Motorola, Shaye Communications**

Status in 1991:   **Consortium withdrawn from telepoint market**

The Mercury Callpoint consortium gained a telepoint operating licence in 1989. Mercury Communications entered the market in order to add another aspect to its telecommunications product range, having already built up a significant landline business. By acquiring a 'mobile arm', Mercury would compete with BT on all levels. Motorola and Shaye joined the consortium as organisations able to provide expertise in equipment manufacture and base station development. For Mercury, it was considered important to include such experience in their consortium, as it believed that licences would only be given out to groups of organisations with experience in these areas of mobile communications operation. For Motorola and Shaye themselves, both planned to produce equipment for the telepoint market and may have joined the Mercury consortium hoping to benefit from feedback they would gain as an operator. The composition of the Mercury Callpoint consortium appeared to be technology based.

Mercury Callpoint launched an initial telepoint service in December 1989, to which market response was disappointing. Differences may have arisen because the equipment manufacturers could have encountered difficulties in working with other telepoint consortia, whilst being linked to the Mercury consortium. Mercury Communications, which was initially optimistic concerning the prospects for telepoint, became increasingly uncertain of the future for the technology, an uncertainty also shared by Motorola. Mercury Callpoint approached BYPS to talk about a possible merger between the two organisations, but these talks failed.

By agreement the three Mercury Callpoint partners decided to wind down operations in July 1991 and withdraw from the telepoint market. For Mercury Communications, the withdrawal means that it can concentrate on the PCN and landline market, where it is also involved. For Motorola and Shaye, there is no longer a need to reconcile the dual roles of equipment manufacturer and consortium participant.

Case 2: BYPS

Original consortium participants:	**Barclays Bank, Philips, Shell Oil**
Status in 1991:	**Consortium taken over by Hutchison Telecommunications. Barclays taken 5% stake in Hutchison Telecommunications**

The BYPS consortium also gained a telepoint operating licence in 1989. Philips was the organisation behind the formation of the consortium which also consisted of Barclays and Shell. The entire consortium was put together in a relatively short time. Although Philips felt that it had the technical expertise necessary to submit a telepoint licence bid, Shell and Barclays were approached as providers of base station sites.

The BYPS consortium in this form did not launch a telepoint service. This telepoint operation was acquired by Hutchison Telecommunications in February 1991. Hutchison Telecommunications is part of Hutchison Whampoa, a Hong Kong based conglomerate controlled by Li Ka-shing, a Chinese entrepreneur. Hutchison Whampoa is a highly profitable and powerful group, with assets of over £3 billion. Its Hutchison Telecommunications subsidiary has extensive operating experience and enjoys considerable success in Hong Kong, and the purchase of the BYPS telepoint consortium is part of a significant and wide-ranging programme of investment in UK mobile communications. This

has included the purchase of Quadrant Communications, a cellular radio service provider, and the takeover of the cellular and paging businesses of Millicom in the UK. Hutchison Telecommunications has also invested in a UK mobile data service and has purchased the Microtel PCN consortium. Hutchison Telecommunications (UK) is now valued at £150 million (21).

The acquisition came after Philips, faced with considerable and unexpected decline in its overall profitability, made a decision to dispense with all peripheral business ventures in order to concentrate on core activity. This meant a withdrawal from the telepoint consortium. At about this time, the merger discussions between Mercury Callpoint and BYPS occurred, but the merger did not go ahead. Hutchison had become involved with Barclays in a separate business venture in the UK in 1989 and was interested in replacing the missing shareholder as part of its wider strategic move into the UK telecommunications market. In fact, Hutchison purchased the whole BYPS telepoint operation.

Case 3: Unitel

Original consortium participants: **STC, US West, Thorn EMI, Deutsche Bundespost**

Status in 1991: **Deutsche Bundespost withdrawn from consortium.**
STC taken over by Northern Telecom and reviewing stake.
Unitel consortium to carry out joint network development with Mercury PCN

The Unitel consortium was awarded a PCN licence in December 1989. The consortium included organisations with telecommunications operating experience, as it was believed that such experience was needed in order to gain a licence. STC became the official project

leader, having existing expertise in UK telecommunications. US West has experience in operating cellular radio in the US.

Since the licence was awarded to Unitel, a number of changes have occurred in the consortium composition. Deutsche Bundespost has withdrawn, citing commitments in Eastern Europe as precluding its ability to play a financial role in UK PCN development. Northern Telecom has acquired STC and is reviewing its investment in Unitel. The remaining two participants - Thorn EMI and US West - remain committed to PCN. However, some doubts have emerged as to the cost of infrastructure development, leading to an agreement with the Mercury PCN consortium to carry out joint network development. The two organisations state that they will continue to carry out 'separate' PCN marketing.

Case 4: Microtel

Original consortium: participants:	**British Aerospace, Pacific Telesis, Matra, Millicom, Sony**
Status in 1991:	**Pacific Telecom, Matra, Millicom, Sony withdrawn from consortium. Consortium taken over by Hutchison Telecommunications. British Aerospace taken 30% stake in Hutchison Telecommunications.**

Microtel was also awarded a PCN licence in December 1989. The consortium was originally led by British Aerospace, which considered PCN to provide a strategic opportunity to compete with BT at all levels. British Aerospace formed a consortium at a late stage. Matra was approached as an organisation which had already worked on European cellular radio infrastructure. Matra joined Microtel expecting to become a preferred supplier of base stations. Both Millicom and Pacific Telesis had existing links with British Aerospace and were approached on the basis that both had network operating experience, Millicom as a

partner in the Cellnet cellular radio consortium. Sony joined the consortium as an organisation with extensive experience in consumer marketing.

Since consortium formation, Millicom, Pacific Telesis, Sony and Matra have all withdrawn, selling their stakes to British Aerospace. This is indicative of a realisation amongst organisations that there are uncertainties surrounding the development of the PCN market and that the original forecasts made for PCN market growth do not appear to be as promising in the light of recent developments in the mobile communications sector.

Hutchison bought the Microtel operation from British Aerospace in July 1991. It is claimed that Hutchison plans to use the Microtel purchase as a springboard for further expansion into continental Europe, including the formation of a consortium for a bid for a PCN licence in Germany (22).

It is clear that in the case of both PCNs and telepoint, consortia participants had to respond quickly to the opportunities to apply for licences, and interest was undoubtedly extensively generated by the rapid growth and high returns flowing from investments in cellular technology. Given time for greater analysis and reflection, the short term prospects may not have appeared so favourable causing some to reappraise their commitment to mobile communications.

We now aim to discuss each of the propositions in the light of developments in mobile communications. In doing so, we are focusing in particular on the collaborations amongst the prime suppliers of the services (telepoint and PCN), recognising that these are

realistically only components of the total networks. The research underway is extending the analysis to consider other parties such as the suppliers of hardware.

DISCUSSION

Mobile communications illustrates a number of features about technological development in 'nascent' sectors. We discuss these with reference to the six propositions advanced earlier.

Proposition 1: **The rapid pace of change in nascent sectors implies that entrepreneurial action tends to be the initial spur to development.**

The evidence of the responses of fifteen participants in the consortia which were awarded licenses does not unambiguously support the proposition. Only five viewed their entry into 'mobile communications' as in any sense 'entrepreneurial', with nine regarding entry as generally 'cautiously managed'. One respondent saw his company's entry as neither clearly one nor the other.

When asked to differentiate between whether or not entry involved detailed planning or was the result of a 'prompt' response, only six saw their company's approach as compatible with the former, and eight classified entry in terms of the latter. Again, one respondent regarded his company as somewhere between the two.

Two comments can perhaps be made. First, responses may be affected by whether or not the business had previous experience in telecommunications. Those with some prior

involvement may be expected to have undertaken analyses and to have objectives regarding some aspect of telecommunications. Entry into mobile communications may be construed as a natural extension, a continuation of its technological trajectory, and therefore might be seen as logical and planned. Indeed, ten respondents regarded the mobile communications sector as related to existing business activities. Second, in a tradition which places favourable emphasis on the virtues of the 'scientific' approach to problem solving and therefore regards methodologies based on logic, rationality and planning as superior, it would not be surprising that executives would wish to project their own decision making as agreeing with this perspective. The fact is that there was only limited time to respond to the Government's invitation to bid for licences, that there was little experience of mobile communications on which to base a realistic view of its future potential and that inevitably decisions must have been founded on speculation and wishful thinking.

Proposition 2: **Collaboration is regarded as increasingly important for product development**.

In the contemporary literature, there is much on the value and indeed the necessity of collaboration in product development (14). In biotechnology, recent research highlights the important role that collaboration has assumed in order to achieve both research and commercial goals (23). A recent study by Laredo points to the extent of collaborative activity (although not exclusively with regard to product development) (24). Pre-competitive research initiatives such as those encouraged by the European Commission have stimulated collaboration. *Prima facie*, it would appear that in general co-operation can enhance efficiency and effectiveness but a detailed systematic analysis is required.

27

Proposition 3: **The development of networks will be primarily opportunistic**.

The early formation of the networks by the participating businesses may well have followed a pattern akin to the original entry into the sector.

Partnerships may have been forged between those who were available and were known to those involved, although it is obvious that previous relationships were influential in some cases.

Proposition 4: **Technological and product development is the essential driver of nascent new technology sectors**.

The initial focus tended to be on the development of the technology, the product and the necessary infrastructure. Market analyses were undertaken but were essential macro in nature and generally based on secondary data. It is interesting in this context, that ten of the fifteen respondents to the mail questionnaire perceived market uncertainty as significant (four saw uncertainty as neither high nor low; and one was relatively certain about the market). On the other hand, nine were certain about the ability to develop the technology, with five seeing some uncertainty about the technology. Perhaps it is natural, and of course easier, to focus on what one feels relatively sure about. Telepoint illustrates how customer values were given relatively little regard.

28

TELEPOINT IN THE UK: A CASE STUDY

Of the four consortia licensed to provide telepoint services in the UK, three - Phonepoint, Mercury Callpoint and Ferranti Creditphone - launched a telepoint service in 1989 or 1990. The launch was beset with difficulties. First, the three competing systems were incompatible, although a second generation standardised technology was promised at a later date. This meant that a handset to be used on one specific network could not be used on any of the other networks. To register with a second network, a second phone had to be purchased. With the advent of the promised second generation technology, the Common Air Interface (CAI) standard, this non-standardisation *was* close to being resolved by the operators before they withdrew from the market. However, some considerable damage was done by the initial customer confusion resulting from the launch of these three incompatible systems and this must be countered by the possibly remaining operator, Hutchison, which has yet to enter the 'telepoint' market.

Second, the initial launch of the service was carried out without the necessary back-up infrastructure. None of the telepoint operators had invested in an adequate network of base stations. Telepoint was in essence still a concept. This had implications for much of the initial marketing effort and for the cash flow of the pioneering telepoint operators. The necessity of having a substantial infrastructure in place before promoting the service is crucial if customers are to be able to see the service demonstrated in action.

Third, and perhaps most significantly in the long term, the telepoint operators paid little consideration to whether the telepoint technology was offering appreciable customer values.

Early telepoint services were aimed at business people and this involved the acceptance of the one-way nature of the service and, to an extent, the embracing of a street culture by executives. It may be that the telepoint operators did not pay sufficient attention to whether or not the technology was offering significant intrinsic benefits. If this is not the case, telepoint will not be adopted, especially at a time when recessionary pressures are causing re-evaluation of non-essential spending. It may be that in order to encourage market acceptance, the remaining telepoint operator will need to enhance the functions of the technology (for instance, making it two-way instead of one-way); pay careful attention to competitive pricing; and consider changes in the telepoint concept, such as the development of neighbourhood telepoint and telepoint PABX systems. It might also be appropriate to make a re-assessment of the target markets for the telepoint service and consider innovative potential user groups at which telepoint may be aimed.

The failure of the telepoint operators to make sufficient consideration of customer values in product development so far is demonstrated by the results of a survey carried out of potential telepoint users in 1990 as part of the research programme. 78 responses were received to a questionnaire sent out to senior communications managers in 200 major UK organisations. Use of telepoint was found to be low - only 12% of respondent organisations had registered with a telepoint network. However, this was expected to be the case at the time of the survey, as telepoint was still only newly launched. Of more interest were the perceptions of the telepoint service held by respondents. Significantly, the majority of managers expressed concern over the incompatibility of the three telepoint systems on the market at the time, the lack of base stations and the intrinsic disadvantages of the telepoint technology for business users. (See Tables 2 and 3).

Table 2: **Risks of Purchasing Telepoint in 1990 as Perceived by Communications Managers**

	% of Respondents Rating as a 'Highly Significant' Risk
The network chosen will become obsolete with the introduction of the CAI standard	80%
Base station numbers will not increase quickly to an acceptable level	75%

Table 3: **Perceptions of the Telepoint Service in 1990 Held by Communications Managers**

	% of Respondents 'Strongly Agreeing' with the Statement
The absence of a universal standard is a major hinderance to the more widespread adoption of telepoint	89%
The potential telepoint purchaser is likely to be confused by the existence of three incompatible telepoint networks	85%
There is little or no business interest in telepoint as a one-way service only	63%

The attitude of managers towards telepoint in 1990 is further demonstrated by the following statements made by questionnaire respondents.

"Telepoint is under evaluation only at this stage as (it has) questionable use for the group and doubts as to whether the service will exist in the mid to longer term." (Respondent A)

"I do not savour the prospect of standing in the street surrounded by crowds/lorries/buses/cars trying to hold a conversation. I perceive no business use of value for telepoint as needs are better served by other communications facilities, private and public." (Respondent B)

"(In our organisation) there is no place for telepoint. We require mobile users to be contactable with instant reply." (Respondent C)

Thus, it is clear that there has been somewhat of a failure on the part of the telepoint operators to fully embrace the customer perspective of the service. Whereas customer difficulties with the initial incompatibility of networks and the lack of base stations are fairly easily remedied, the widely held dissatisfaction with the telepoint concept itself is more difficult to rectify.

Proposition 5: **Networks in nascent new technology sectors are intrinsically unstable.**

Proposition 6: **There will be a consolidation of the network over time, with a coalescence around stronger parties.**

As expected the evidence seems to confirm the view that chance and the often spontaneous and somewhat frenetic activity of many in embryonic sectors may lead to formation of market and network positions that are not as well considered as they might be. It is also clear that much remains to be discovered and developed. With organisational learning, greater information and intelligence, and more time for reflection it is only to be expected that there will be re-evaluation. Tensions may be uncovered in, for example, established relationships. New, more relevant parties may enter the frame.

The history to date of the collaborations in both telepoint and PCNs points to an inherent instability in parts of the network. This may be partly attributed to a profound reappraisal of the prospects for personal mobile communications, causing some to withdraw. External influences can obviously be powerful determinants of network development and construction. New entrants such as Hutchison can also have a disequilibriating impact.

32

At quite an early stage, the network organisations involved in mobile communications at the 'service' supply level are undergoing considerable rationalisation. It may well be that the UK Government's concern with competition resulted in the award of too many licenses in the first instance. Rationalisation would be an inevitable consequence. The nature and orientation of the 'consolidation' must however be of some interest. It may be influenced by the not mutually exclusive trends of globalisation, the significant economies of scale in electronics (a base technology for telecommunications) and the dominant position, often founded on considerable experience, of certain players. These may include the suppliers of electronic hardware (such as the handsets) which may be able to, for example, override the particular requirements of individual service suppliers because of advantages derived from economies of scale and of scope. In a sense, the network, certainly in the case of mobile communications, may effectively come under the influence of a few major suppliers (25) and in this sense technological development is 'cartellised'.

Overall, the study of mobile communications suggests that:

-   entrepreneurial swarming has been a significant feature of its early phase of evolution, and that this will inevitably affect the nature of 'networking' activity;

-   networks had a built-in instability flowing from the stochastic and action-based approach to network formation, and there would appear to be a need for a more detailed analysis on 'interactions' and networks in such nascent-like sectors;

activity has tended to be technology/product dominated, and therefore the means of introducing a perspective concerned with customer values needs to be more deeply considered. The appointment of marketing specialists in fast moving consumer products is not necessarily an adequate solution either to some fundamental disadvantages of a technology or a strategy based on assumptions which were formulated on extrapolations of past experience, an intrinsic belief in the values of the technology and sheer wishful thinking (26).

34

Appendix

Changes in Telepoint and PCN Operating Consortia Between Formation and 1991

Consortium	Original Members	Status in 1991
Phonepoint	British Telecom Northern Telecom (formally STC) Deutsche Bundespost France Telecom Nynex	Withdrawn from market
Mercury Callpoint	Mercury Communications Motorola Shaye Communications	Withdrawn from market
BYPS	Barclays Philips Shell	Philips withdrew from consortium, entire consortium taken over by Hutchison Telecommunications. Barclays has 5% stake in Hutchison
Ferranti Creditphone	Ferranti Minor venture capitalists	Withdrawn from market
Mercury PCN	Mercury Communications Motorola Telefonica	Mercury Communications has bought out stakes of other two players. Joint infrastructure development with Unitel.
Unitel	US West Thorn EMI Northern Telecom (formally STC) Deutsche Bundespost	Deutsche Bundespost withdrawn from consortium, Northern Telecom may follow. US West and Thorn EMI still committed. Joint infrastructure development with Mercury PCN.
Microtel	British Aerospace Pacific Telesis Millicom Sony Matra	Pacific Telesis, Millicom, Sony and Matra all sold stake to British Aerospace, before British Aerospace sold entire operation to Hutchison Telecommunications. British Aerospace has 30% stake in Hutchison

35

References

1. METCALFE S. & GIBBONS M. 1989
    "Technology, Variety and Organisations" in Research on Technological Innovation Management and Policy, Vol. 4, pp153-193, JAI Press.

2. SCHUMPETER J. 1943
    Capitalism, Socialism and Democracy, (Unwin Edition).

3. HAKANSSON H. 1987
    Industrial Technological Development: A Network Approach, Beckenham, Croom Helm.

4. JARILLO J.C. 1988
    "On Strategic Networks" Strategic Management Journal, Vol. 9, pp31-41.

5. VON HIPPEL E. 1978
    "A Customer Active Paradigm for Industrial Product Idea Generation", Research Policy, Vol. 7, pp240-266.

6. FREEMAN C. 1982
    "The Economics of Industrial Innovation", 2nd edition, Frances Pinter.

7. MYERS S. & MARQUIS D.G. 1969
    "Successful Industrial Innovation", National Science Foundation, Washington, pp 69-71.

8. CENTRE FOR THE STUDY OF INDUSTRIAL INNOVATION 1972
    "Success and Failure in Industrial Innovation", February.

9. LANGRISH J. et al, 1972
    "Wealth from Knowledge", Macmillan.

10. COOPER R.G. 1979
    "Identifying Industrial New Product Success: Project New Product", Industrial Marketing Management, Vol. 8, pp124-135.

11. ROTHWELL R. 1977
    "The Characteristics of Successful Innovators and Technically Progressive Firms (with some comments on innovation research)", R&D Management, Vol. 7 No. 3, pp191-206.

12. MCKENNA R. 1991
    "Marketing is Everything", Harvard Business Review, January/February, pp65-79.

13. AXELSSON B. & HAKANSSON H. 1990
    "The Development Role of Purchasing in an Internationally Oriented Company" in Ford, D. (ed) Understanding Business Markets: Interaction, Relationships and Networks, London, Academic Press.

36

14. LITTLER D.A. & WILSON D.F. 1991
"Strategic Alliancing in Computerised Business Systems", <u>Technovation</u>, Vol. 11 No. 8, pp457-73.

15. GRINYER P.H. & SPENDER J-C. 1979
"Recipes, Crises and Adaptation in Mature Businesses", <u>International Studies of Management and Organisation</u>, Vol. 9, No. 3, pp113-133.

16. LITTLER D.A. LEVERICK F. BRUCE M. & WILSON D. 1992
"On Sector Paradigms", Manchester Marketing Research Series, forthcoming.

17. LITTLER D.A. & SWEETING R.C. 1989
<u>Management Accounting: The Challenge of Technological Innovation</u>, London, The Chartered Institute of Management Accountants.

18. NELSON R.R. & WINTER S.G. 1977
"In Search of Useful Theory of Innovation", <u>Research Policy</u>, Vol. 6, pp36-76.

19. OECD/DSTI 1986
"STI Indicators Newsletter", No. 9, Paris, OECD.

20. ABRAHAMS P. 1991
"Mercury Callpoint Blames Excessive Competition for Failure", <u>Financial Times</u>, July.

21. FOSTER A. 1991
"On Line to be Big in Personal Communications", <u>Financial Times</u>, July, p20.

22. LORENZ A. 1991
"Hutchison Harbours Big Ambitions", <u>The Sunday Times</u>, July.

23. BURRILL G.S. & THE ERNST AND YOUNG HIGH TECHNOLOGY GROUP 1989
<u>Biotech 90: Into the Next Decade</u>, Mary Ann Liebert, New York.

24. LAREDO P. 1989
"Taking Advantage of 1992 - The Impact of the Single European Market on High Technology Business". In the proceedings of the KPMG 1991 Conference for High Technology Business, London, Graham and Trotman.

25. LITTLER D.A. & SHARP B. 1990
"Prospects for Competition in a Pan-European Cellular System" in Locksley, G. <u>Information technologies in the Single European Market</u>, London, Frances Pinter.

26. LITTLER D.A. & LEVERICK F. 1992
"The Elusiveness of Customer Values", PICT Policy Paper, forthcoming.

Çocuklar çok heyecanlıydı. Tarık'ın annesinin karnının git git büyüdüğünü görmüşlerdi. Herkes o büyük günü bekliyordu.

The children were excited. They had seen Tariq's mum getting bigger and bigger and bigger. They had been waiting for the big day.

"Çantada ne var Tarık?" diye sordu öğretmeni, Bayan Smith.
"Annem herkese dağıtmam için bu hurmaları verdi. Yeni doğan
bebeklere yumuşak bir hurma parçası veririz. Tadıcağı ilk şey bu olur."

"What's in the bag, Tariq?" asked his teacher, Miss Smith.
"My mum gave me these dates to share with everyone. We give a
new baby a soft piece of date, the first thing they will ever taste."

Bütün çocuklar birer hurma yedi.
Çok tatlı ve yumuşaktı.

The children all had a date.
Hmmm, it tasted sweet and smooth.

Çocuklar okulda beş hissi öğrenmişlerdi ve tatmak, dokunmak, görmek, duymak ve koklamak hakkında herşeyi biliyorlardı.

The children had been learning about the five senses in school and they all knew about tasting, touching, seeing, hearing and smelling.

"Son son kaçınızın bir erkek ya da kız kardeşi oldu?"
diye sordu Bayan Smith.
Birçok parmak havaya kalktı.

"How many of you have had a new baby brother or sister recently?"
asked Miss Smith.
Quite a few hands shot up.

"Herkes annesine babasına yeni doğan bebeklerin nasıl karşılandığını sorsun. Belki Cuma günü bizlere birşeyler getirip anlatabilirsiniz," dedi Bayan Smith.

"Can you ask your parents how you welcome new babies in your family? Maybe you can all bring something in on Friday and tell us about it," said Miss Smith.

"Herhangi birşey getirebilirmiyiz?" dedi Ben.
"Evet Ben. Beş hislerle ilgili olduğu sürece
herhangi birşey olabilir!"

"Can we bring anything?" asked Ben.
"Yes, Ben. Anything you like, as long as it's to do
with the five senses!"

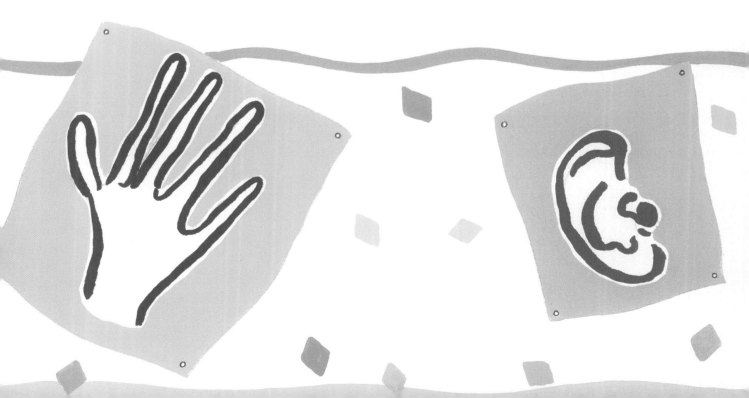

Cuma günü bütün çocuklar özel
birşeyler getirdiler.
Bayan Smith onları bir çember
şeklinde oturtturdu.
"Evet çocuklar," diye başladı. "Çoğumuz
aileye yeni bir bebeğin katılmasının ne
kadar harika birşey olduğunu biliyoruz. Herkes
için sevinç ve coşku dolu bir zamandır. Şimdi
başkalarının evinde yeni bir bebek olmanın nasıl
birşey olduğunu görelim."

On Friday, all the children came to school with something extra special.
Miss Smith sat them down in a circle.
"Now children," she began. "Many of us know how wonderful it is to have
a new baby in the family. For everyone it's a time of great joy and
celebration. Let's find out what it's like to be a new baby in
each other's homes."

"An-Mei, sizin evde yeni bir bebek doğunca ne olur anlat bakalım," diye sordu Bayan Smith.
Çok dikktalice An-Mei bir yumurta çıkardı, küçük bir yumurta, kırmızıya boyanmış.

"So, An-Mei, what happens when a new baby is born in your house?" she asked.
Very carefully An-Mei brought out an egg, a little egg, painted red.

"Bu annemin ve babamın dostlarımıza ve akrabalarımıza hediye olarak verdiği yumurtalardan biri. Bol şans getirmesi için kırmızı boyanmıştır. Yumurta doğumu, hayatı ve büyümeyi simgeler. Ellerinizle dokunun," dedi ve yumurtayı Brian'a verdi.

"This is one of the eggs that my mum and dad gave as gifts to our family and friends. It is painted red, the colour of good luck. The egg stands for birth, life and growth. Touch it with your hands," she said, passing it to Brian.

"Çok pürüzsüz, tıpkı annemin yüzü gibi,"
dedi Brian yumurtaya dokunarak.
Diğer çocuklar gülümsedi.
"Peki, sırada kim var?" diye sordu
Bayan Smith.

"It's so smooth, just like my mum's
face," said Brian, stroking the cool little egg.
The other children all smiled.
"Now, who's next?" asked Miss Smith.

Saida yavaşça küçük beyaz bir zarfı açtı ve içinden bir tutam şaç çıkardı, beyaz bir kurdele ile bağlanmış bir tutam kıvırcık siyah saç.

Slowly, Saida opened a small white envelope and took out a lock of hair, a lock of curly dark hair, tied with a white ribbon.

"Yedi günlükken Amma ve Abba erkek kardeşimin saçlarını
traşladıktan sonra sakladıkları saçın birazı bu."
"Niye?" diye sordu Ben.
"Kuyumcuya götürüp tarttırdıktan sonra ağırlığı kadar gümüş
alıp yoksullara dağıtmak için," dedi Saida.

"This is some of my baby brother's first hair that was kept after Amma
and Abba shaved my brother's head, when he was only seven days old."
"Why?" asked Ben.
"So that they could take it to the jewellers and weigh it. Then they gave
its weight in silver to help the poor," said Saida.

Caroline'a verdi. "Parmaklarınla hisset," dedi. "Erkek kardeşimin ilk saçı."

"Çok hafif ve yumuşacık," dedi Caroline saç tutamını okşayarak.

She passed it to Caroline. "Feel it with your fingers," she said. "My baby brother's first hair..."

"It's so light and soft," Caroline said, stroking the little curl.

Sonra Dimitri'nin sırası geldi. Küçük bir
kutu açtı. İçinde karanlık kutuda
parıldayan paralar vardı,
gümüş ve altın paralar.

Next it was Dimitri's turn. He opened a small box.
In it were coins, gold and silver coins,
shining in the dark box.

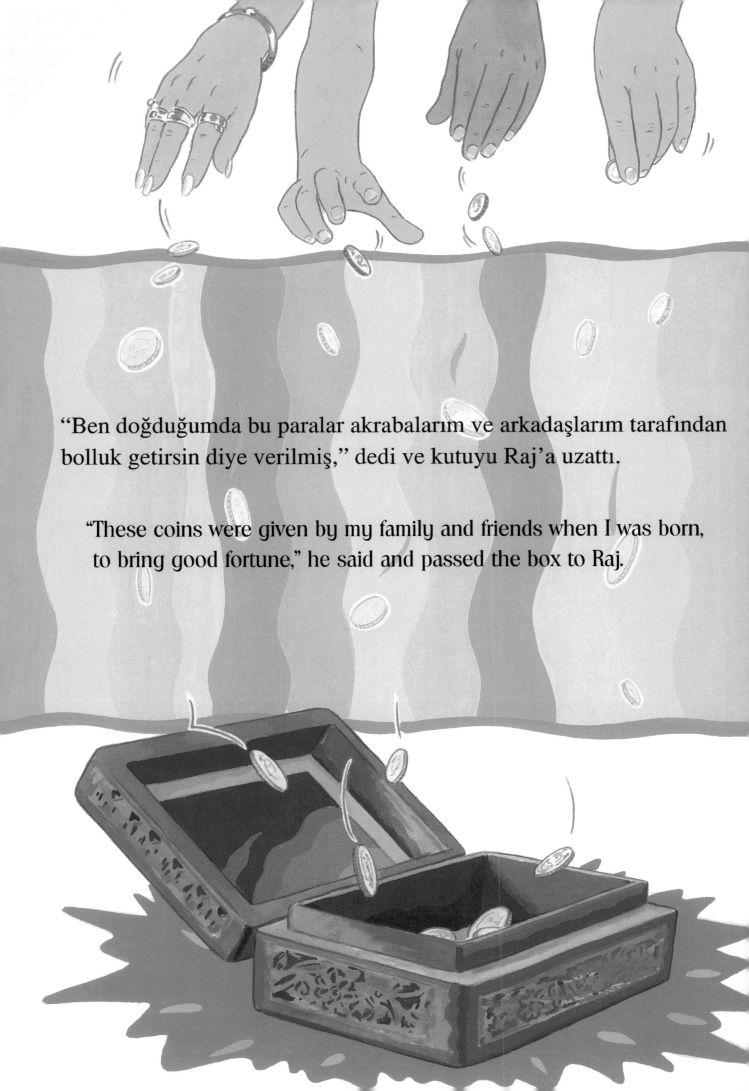

"Ben doğduğumda bu paralar akrabalarım ve arkadaşlarım tarafından bolluk getirsin diye verilmiş," dedi ve kutuyu Raj'a uzattı.

"These coins were given by my family and friends when I was born, to bring good fortune," he said and passed the box to Raj.

"Kutuyu oynat ve paraların çıkardığı sesi dinle," dedi Dimitri.
"Çangur çungur ses çıkıyor!" dedi Raj kutuyu kulağına yaklaştırarak.

"Shake the box and listen to the sound the coins make."
"It jingle-jangles!" cried Raj, putting his ear close to the box.

Çekinerek Nadia konuştıu.
"Öğretmenim," dedi. "Benim de göstermek istediğim birşey var."
Bir poşetin içinden kocaman ve sıcacık görünüşlü çok sevgi
görmüş bir kazak çıkarttı.

Nadia spoke up, shyly.
"Miss," she said, "I've got something."
She picked up a bag and pulled out
a jumper, a big warm jumper that looked
as though it had seen a lot of love.

"Bu babamın kazağı," dedi. "Doğduğumda beni buna sarmışlar ve bana üç tane özel isim vermişler."

"This is my dad's jumper," she said. "When I was born, I was wrapped in it, and given three special names."

Kazağı Sara'ya verdi.
"Gözlerini kapa ve kokla," diye fısıldadı.
"Babam gibi güçlü ve güvenli kokuyor."

She passed it to Sara.
"Close your eyes and smell it," she whispered. "It smells strong and safe like my dad."

Sara gözlerini kapadı ve derin bir nefes aldı.
"Mmmm," diye iç çekti, "yeni doğan bir bebek için
ne kadar hoş bir koku!"

Sara closed her eyes and breathed in deeply.
"Hmmm," she sighed, "what a lovely smell
for a newborn baby!"

Sonunda Elima'nın sırası geldi.

Çantasının içinden bir yaprak çıkardı, bir aloe yaprağı.

"Ben doğduğumda bana biraz bundan vermişler," dedi. "Tadına bak."

Yaprağı sıktı ve Mona'nın parmağına birkaç damla su geldi.

Finally it was Elima's turn.

From his bag, he brought out a leaf, a small aloe leaf.

"When I was born, I was given some of this," he said. "Taste it."

He squeezed it and some juice fell onto Mona's fingers.

Acele ile tattı.

"Ayyy! Çok acı," diye bağırdı ağzını silerek.

Eagerly she tasted it.

"Urghh! It's so bitter," she cried, wiping her mouth.

"Bu bebeğe hayatın acı olabileceğini, ama..." dedi küçük bir kavanoz bal çıkararak, "aynı zamanda da tatlı olabileceğini göstermek için."

"That is to teach the baby that life can be bitter, but..." he said, bringing out a little pot of honey, "it can also be sweet!"

*We do not recommend giving honey to a baby less than a year old, due to potential health risks.

Mona aloe yaprağının acı tadından hemen tatlı baldan bir kaşık alarak kurtuldu.

Mona was quick to get rid of the aloe taste with a spoonful of delicious honey.

"Öğretmenim," dedi Kwesi. "Bütün hislerimizi kullandık, değil mi?" Kocaman bir gülücükle. "Evet, çok haklısın Kwesi," dedi Bayan Smith.

"Miss!" cried Kwesi, "we've used all of our senses, haven't we?"
"That's right, Kwesi," said Miss Smith, with a huge smile on her face.

"Hepinize aferin! Size özel bir armağan olarak
dönem sonunda Beş Hisler Partisi yaparız."
"Oley!" diye sevindi herkes.
"Ve," dedi Bayan Smith, "süpriz bir misafirimiz de olacak."
Herkes bunun kim olabileceğini merak etti.

"Well done, all of you! As a special treat, we'll have a Five Senses party
at the end of term."
"Hooray!" they all cheered.
"And," said Miss Smith, "we'll have a surprise visitor."
They all wondered who that could be.

Dönemin son gününde, bütün çocuklar Beş Hisler Partisinde eğlenirken, biri kapıyı çaldı.
"Bu da kim?" dedi Bayan Smith kocaman bir gülücükle.

On the last day of term, while the children were enjoying their special Five Senses party, there was a knock at the door.
"Who can that be?" asked Miss Smith with a big smile.

Yavaşça kapı açıldı.
Tarık'ın annesi ve kucağında da...yeni bebek!
Çocuklar çok sevindi.
"Dünya'ya hoş geldin bebek, Dünya'ya hoş geldin bebek!"
diye şarkı söylediler.

Slowly the door opened.
It was Tariq's mum with...the new baby!
The children cheered.
"Welcome to the world, baby, welcome to
the world!" they all sang.

Tarık'ın annesi ve bebek kız kardeşi de partiye katıldılar.
Ve biliyormusunuz, bir bebeğin görebileceği en güzel karşılamaydı!

Tariq's mum and his new baby brother came and joined the party.
And do you know, it was the nicest welcome any baby had ever had!